CONQUERING
TOXIC EMOTIONS

Rhonda Favano

ISBN: 978-0-9988534-0-6
Printed in the United States of America
First printing.

Growing Healthy Homes LLC
P.O. Box 3154
Bartlesville, OK 74006

To obtain additional copies of this book, please visit
www.GrowingHealthyHomes.com.

Disclaimer: The information presented in the book is for educational purposes only. It is not intended to diagnose, treat, cure, or prevent any disease or illness. If you have a medical condition, please consult the health care provider of your choice.

The author is not liable for the misuse or misunderstanding of any information contained within this publication.

After extensive research, the author has concluded that Young Living Essential Oils are 100% pure, authentic, and unadulterated. This is supported by their proprietary Seed to Seal® process. The author encourages you to do your own research and be an informed consumer.

I would like to dedicate this book to everyone who struggles with negative, toxic emotions but desires to live a healthy, happy, stress-free life.

Just as I endeavor to educate, empower and inspire my friends, family, acquaintances, and the Anointing Nations Tribe; my prayer is that this book will provide you with many insights that will allow you to conquer emotions (some hidden away for long periods of time), so that you may enjoy a much healthier, more fulfilling lifestyle free from the burden of emotional baggage.

Make your life amazing!

TABLE OF CONTENTS

ACKNOWLEDGEMENTS

This book is proof that with God all things are possible. Through Him, His guidance and unwavering love for me, I am able to share these truths with you.

There are many people who play a huge part in my amazing journey, and to each I am very appreciative.

The Anointing Nations Tribe; you challenge me, you allow me to grow, and you share my extreme passion for a true lifestyle of wellness, purpose and abundance. I love you and am thankful that we have been divinely connected.

There are those who encourage, support and love me unconditionally; these individuals bring me such joy.

First is my husband, Frank. You listen, cheer me on, and you are always in my corner. You are my rock. I love you, and I am excited for the next adventure life brings us.

God blessed me with two creative, generous and loving sons, Brandon and Brett. I am so proud of you both. You make this mama's heart happy! I am so thankful that Brandon and my beautiful daughter-in-love, Jennifer, have risen to, and accepted the challenge of being great parents to my precious granddaughters.

My beautiful girls who melt my heart with their precious smiles, hugs and sweet declarations of "I love you Grandma": Kynzee, Porscha and Aspyn, I love you infinity.

There are two precious people who inspired me to pursue the possibilities within each bottle of Young Living Essential Oils. Dr. David and Lee Stewart, thank you for imparting a curiosity, love and passion for God's provision for us.

To my YL family, Laura Hopkins, Karen Hopkins and Jan Collins, thank you for your help in bringing this book to the world. I appreciate your support, mentoring and patience.

To my friends who believed I could actually write a book that would help people, Terri and Buddy Black, thank you.

Thank you Fara, Katie and Elizabeth Clough for ensuring I had a great picture for this book. Love you girls.

FOREWORD

"Dr. Favano has created a wonderful and useful resource for anyone and everyone interested in the beneficial uses of essential oils. The chemistry and multitude of practical applications of essential oils is an expansive topic involving every aspect of our health—physically, emotionally, and spiritually. Dr. Favano has succeeded in creating an easy-to-use guide to essential oils that is relevant in all aspects of our lives, and one that will be useful to beginners as well as to seasoned professionals in the aromatherapy field.

A new comer to essential oils can take this wonderful book and immediately find good ways to use them and enjoy their benefits right from the start. At the same time, experienced long-time users of the oils will discover new insights and ways to utilize them.

I have been using and teaching about essential oils for 18 years, and I still found new benefits and insights in Dr. Favano's book that I had not yet encountered.

Thank you, Rhonda for your gift to the world."

—David Stewart, PhD, DNM
Author of 16 books, including Healing Oils of the Bible
Founder & President of CARE, Center for Aromatherapy Research and Education

"Within just a few pages I knew I loved Rhonda Favano's writing style; light and genuine yet packed with powerful content! After reading many books on emotions and essential oils, I think this may just be my new favorite. It is short, concise, and easily read in one sitting. The protocols are easy to find and organized in an understandable manner. I can't wait to buy this in bulk and share it with everyone!"

—Sonya Swan, Young Living Diamond, Entrepreneur, Speaker

"Once people realize the importance of emotional freedom related to their overall health, they want to know: where do I start? Rhonda, through her clinical and personal experiences, teaches us how and more in a simple, compassionate, and factual style with which anyone can relate. Keeping this guide in my purse is like having her servant's heart and beautiful mind right there to encourage me in my personal walk and bring others along too."

—Laura Hopkins, Young Living Diamond

INTRODUCTION

Once Upon A Time…
When I was a little girl, we used to go to my Grandma's house for Christmas. I vividly recall the smell of pine emanating from the Christmas tree and cinnamon and fresh baked bread wafting from the kitchen where Grandma was making scrumptious cinnamon rolls. All my aunts, uncles, and cousins would arrive, and we would have a grand time playing together. Christmas' at Grandma's house are my happiest childhood memories.

Those days are long gone, and sadly, so is Grandma. Any time I smell cinnamon rolls or the pine scent of a Christmas tree, I am immediately filled with the same joy, love and wonder of those moments at Grandma's. If I close my eyes, I feel like I am there, reliving those precious times!

Just as strong as the smell of pine brings back positive memories, on the opposite spectrum, the smell of smoke causes my stomach to hurt and, at times, even makes me nauseous.

My father was a wheat farmer. During harvest one year, I was burning trash and some of the embers blew out of the barrel. Within minutes, the fire was spreading toward the fuel tanks and wheat fields. As panic ensued, I felt as if someone had hit me in the stomach, and nausea quickly followed. Whenever I smell smoke today, I experience the same abdominal pain and sometimes nausea as I am brought back to that terrifying negative experience.

As I grew into an adult, I realized there was a connection between emotions and well-being. I have observed that happy people are healthier than people who are sad. Those who have more negative emotions seemed to experience more sickness and disease.

This book is a labor of love to empower each of us to maintain healthy emotional balance. As we learn to recognize the effect emotions have on our health, it will encourage us to proactively address and actually release them once and for all. As we become intentional about doing this, our quality of life will greatly improve. We will be happier, more content. Those around us will be delighted as well!

Having personally experienced the effect of holding negative emotions too long, it is my utmost desire to see you set free from this downward spiral. As you read my book, I pray that you walk in health, abundance, and emotional freedom.

Love and Blessings,

Rhonda

"Your success and happiness lies in you. Resolve to keep happy, and your joy and you shall form an invincible host against difficulties."
—Helen Keller

IMPORTANT INFORMATION

The source matters, therefore the only essential oils I use and recommend are Young Living. This company has been providing truly unadulterated essential oils for over 20 years. As I refer to essential oils and therapeutic grade essential oils in this book, I am referring to compounds steam distilled or cold pressed from organic living plant materials such as the flowers, fruits, seeds, roots, bark, leaves, stems, and branches. I am thankful for Young Living's proprietary Seed to Seal® process and their commitment to bring therapeutic grade essential oils to the world. They are the only company that has this. Sadly, many more essential oils are sold than are produced annually, thus they are adulterated and/or synthetic and not a viable option for myself or my family.

THE EMOTIONAL PHYSIOLOGY CONNECTION

As you can see from my personal recount of the two events from my childhood, smells have a profound effect on both our emotions and physiology. Unresolved emotional experiences are recorded in cellular memory (DNA) and remain there as live programming until they are dealt with. These unresolved emotions can be stored anywhere within the body.

I have spent a significant amount of time exploring emotions in my quest to better understand this phenomenon of emotions having effects on our physical body. At one point, I found myself very sick, which led to a strong curiosity of why some people get sick and remain sick, some become healthy again, and others don't get sick at all.

Along this journey, one of my most important discoveries was how our emotions affect us on every level of our being. Because I believe that God created us as multi-dimensional beings with free will, this insight made perfect sense to me. Your emotions can build a good foundation for health and wellness, or they can create disease.

My studies have led me to understand that there are three aspects or levels that make humans multi-dimensional. Those three aspects cannot function alone, and each impacts the other.

These dimensions are comprised of:

- Body—this is our physical being.
- Mind/Soul—our mental realm, will, emotions, thoughts.
- Spirit—our connection to God our creator; our heart; the highest aspect of who we are.

In order to understand how emotions can have a positive or negative effect on our body, let's take a look at the definition of emotion:

1. *Any of the feelings of joy, sorrow, fear, hate, love, etc. ...*
2. *Any strong agitation of the feelings actuated by experiencing love, hate, fear, etc. and usually accompanied by certain physiological changes, as increased heartbeat or respiration and often-overt manifestation, as crying or shaking.*[1]

Wow! There it is in print—***emotions may cause physiological changes***! This explains so much. Your emotions may cause your body to move out of what is known by the medical field as homeostasis. Homeostasis is defined as any self-regulating process by which biological systems remain stable, while adjusting to conditions that are optimal for survival.[2] If homeostasis is successful, life continues; if unsuccessful, disaster or death ensues.

This movement out of homeostasis may be beneficial for short term survival. For example, fight or flight. Some organs may decrease oxygen consumption to provide extra oxygen to the muscles for running. The trigger of this need may be stored and remembered, which will provide for a quicker withdrawal next time. This is an example of how cellular memory and emotional triggers work together to provide a means to maintain safety. Thus, you can see that the importance of maintaining homeostasis as it is crucial to your overall well-being.

The CDC-Kaiser Permanente Adverse Childhood Experiences (ACE) study is one of the largest investigations of childhood experiences and later-life health and well-being. [3]

The original ACE Study was conducted at Kaiser Permanente from 1995 to 1997 with two waves of data collection. Over 17,000 Health Maintenance Organization members from Southern California received physical exams and completed confidential surveys regarding their childhood experiences and current health status and behaviors.

Shockingly, the study revealed that 67% of the adults queried had experienced at least 1 ACE while 80% experienced 2 ACEs.

These are the types of maltreatment the participants experienced:
- Physical abuse
- Sexual abuse
- Psychological abuse
- Physical neglect
- Emotional neglect
- Medical and dental neglect
- Educational neglect
- Inadequate supervision
- Exposure to violent environments

This study uncovered an undeniable link between emotional trauma and physiological issues. It revealed an increase in the following for those who had adverse childhood experiences:
- Early death
- Disease, disability and social problems
- Adoption of health risk behaviors
- Social, emotional and cognitive impairment
- Disrupted neurodevelopment

Understanding this connection between emotions and physical health can initially be a bit of a stretch for some to comprehend, but keep an open mind and try this simple experiment.

Allow yourself to recall a time when you were really scared. Now close your eyes and feel the fear. No, actually ***feel*** the fear. Do you feel it? Now, take note of what is happening in your body.
- Is your heart pounding in your chest?
- Has your breathing become labored?

- Did your neck and shoulders tighten?
- Are you trembling?

I have a friend who was molested as a child and sadly she battled not only depression but had frequent migraines and severe stomachaches as an adult. Once she understood the correlation between suppressed emotions and physical symptoms, she was open to seeking natural solutions to release the negative energy trapped in her body.

Can you recall a time that you experienced an unpleasant physical symptom, such as a headache, stomachache or heart palpitations, when you were angry, afraid or stressed? Like my friend, many people have experienced physical changes in their body from a traumatic emotional occurrence even when nothing physical actually occurred.

Just as fear, anger, and other negative emotions can impact you physiologically, positive emotions can also invoke positive, healthy manifestations.

Remember those feelings when you fell in love for the first time? Perhaps you felt as if you were floating on air and were the happiest person in the entire world. You didn't seem to require as much sleep to feel energized, food tasted better, and that wide smile on your face seemed to be a permanent fixture.

These physical changes in the body are a result of an emotional experience even when nothing physical actually occurs. Experiencing physical reactions in your body to both the negative emotion of fear and the positive emotion of love, it is evident that physical changes are taking place. How does science explain these changes? Science does have a good explanation. It's called energy.

WHAT IS ENERGY?

Energy is an elusive driving force for all physical and chemical changes, and it exists in many forms such as heat, mechanical work (including potential and kinetic energy), light (radiation), sound, electric, and chemical energy. Energy does not have a mass, nor a volume or shape. Thus, energy is very difficult to recognize. However, energy is everywhere.[4]

Law of Vibration
Everything that exists in the universe consists of pure energy which resonates and exists as a vibratory frequency.[5]

We live in a world comprised of energy, vibrations, and frequencies. In this book, these three terms are used interchangeably. All matter, thoughts and emotions have energetic vibrations. Vibrations can be defined as a continuous slight shaking movement or a series of small, fast movements back and forth or from side to side.

"The word vibe comes from the longer word vibrations. In the 'vibrational' world, there are only two kinds of vibrations, positive (+) and negative (-). Every mood or feeling causes you to emit, send-out or offer a vibration, whether positive or negative."[6]

Frequency is defined as the rate at which a vibration occurs that constitutes a wave, either in a material (as in sound waves), or in an electromagnetic field (as in radio waves and light), usually measured per second.[7]

According to what I have learned in physics, matter can't be destroyed, but it can be changed. Consequently, the energy, vibration, or frequency of feelings and emotions can also be altered, and the consequential physical manifestation of an emotion or thought can be changed. If an emotion caused the body to be physically sick, then changing that emotion may result in a physical manifestation of being healed.

It has been discovered that an electromagnetic field, or energy, surrounds the human body. In the next section, you will learn how energy affects your body inside and out.

> ***Everything is energy*** **and that's all there is to it. Match the frequency of the reality you want and you cannot help but get that reality. It can be no other way.**
> ***—Albert Einstein***

Energy Centers

Energy Centers, also known as chakras, are the areas where energy flows through the body. Think of these chakras (or energy centers since the definitions can be used interchangeably) as energy hubs within the body.

Some have questioned the relationship of the word "chakra" to the realm of New Age, a supposed religion that is anti-God. My favorite explanation of chakras is by Dr. David Stewart, PhD in his article, "Are Chakras New Age?":

> *"Chakras are not "New Age." They are Old Age being rediscovered. They are mentioned in both the Old and New Testaments of the Bible. The Jews even have a symbolic representation for the seven Chakras in their Menorah of seven candles, the center one representing the heart chakra.*
>
> *The first thing to understand is that we all possess an electromagnetic field in which our physical bodies are immersed. Even the medical and biological professions acknowledge that human beings have, not only a physical*

body of flesh and fluids, but also a subtle electromagnetic field upon which their physical body is superimposed.

Physicians measure your electromagnetic (EM) field to detect problems with your heart and brain, but they don't understand, nor utilize, the connections of our EM bodies to our physical bodies in a way to provide pathways to healing. They don't understand that physical maladies, conditions, and sicknesses usually show up as irregularities in our EM field before they manifest physically. They are unaware of the connection between our minds and feelings to our electromagnetic field and how the condition of the EM Field affects our physical well-being."[7]

The EKG and EEG are tests that the medical community uses to evaluate the heart and the brain. Usually people don't typically consider that these common medical tests are actually evaluating electrical activity within specific areas of the body. EKGs measure electrical activity of the heartbeat and EEGs are used to detect the electrical activity of the brain.

Did you know that "brain cells" (or intelligence cells) are found not only in the brain but in the heart and gut, as well? I find it fascinating that there is another test called an EGG (Electrogastrogram) that looks at the condition of the colon, or gut. It is another use of energy to "read" the body. Everyone probably knows what it means to have a "gut feeling" and have learned to heed such information from their "gut". This is what I call intuition. You think and make decisions from all three places; brain, heart and colon in your body.

For those that need a biblical visual to chakras, Janet McBride provides a beautiful explanation of the relationship of chakras to the Ancient Menorah in "*Scriptual Essence, Temple Secrets Revealed*":

"The description of the Menorah is a mirror image of the seven electrical energy centers of the spinal column, known as Chakras.

> *These energy points transport the body's electrical frequency through the spine to nourish and strengthen the body systems. The seven chakras represent the Seven-Lamp Menorah of our Temples, transmitting the life-giving Light of God's Spirit. The word "Chakra" is a Sanskrit word from an Ancient Sacred language meaning a wheel."*[8]

As you saw in Janet McBride's description, the seven main chakras are located along the spine extending out the front and back of the body. Each chakra is associated with specific organs and area(s) of the body. The corresponding chakra provides the necessary energy to these areas of the body, allowing for optimal function. Additionally, just as every organ in the human body has its equivalent on the mental and spiritual level, so too each chakra corresponds to a specific aspect of human behavior and development. Dr. Robert O. Becker, M.D. in his book *The Body Electric,* confirms the human body has an electrical frequency and much about a person's health can be determined by it.[9]

As noted earlier, everything in the universe vibrates or has an energetic frequency, including you and I. If you do not feel connected to everything and everyone in your universe, it is because we are not all vibrating at the same frequency.

Can you remember an instance where you met someone for the first time and immediately hit it off or connected with him or her? This is because you are vibrating at the same frequency or energy level as that person is, and as a result you can feel the connection to them.

The degree of openness and flow of energy through your chakras determines your state of well-being and balance. It also determines your ability to relate with other human beings in your space and on your earth. Knowledge of your invisible energy system empowers us to maintain balance and harmony on the physical, mental, and spiritual level. This resonates truth, as you recall that you were created a multi-dimensional being, spirit, soul and body, by the Creator of all.

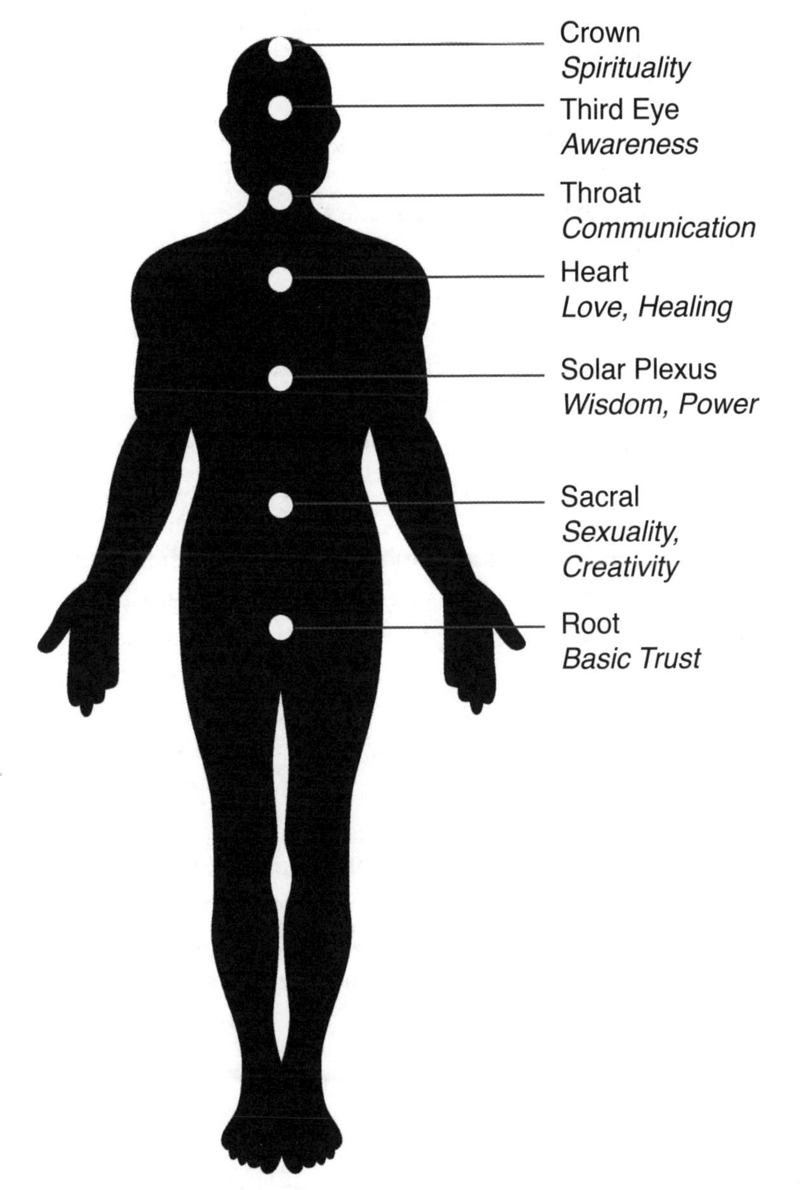

ENERGY AND THOUGHTS

The Bible tells us that God is light. (1 John 1:5) By definition light is electromagnetic radiation within a certain portion of the electromagnetic spectrum.[10] Light is energy. Light energy makes up about 99% of the body's atoms and cells. This energy is used to signal all body parts to carry out their God-given assignments.

What is the connection between energy and thoughts? Thoughts can be described as the action or the process of thinking. It is the product of mental activity. To take action is paramount to needing energy.

Proverbs 23:7 says, "For as he thinks in his heart, so he is." Our thoughts are more important than we realize. According to the Bible, thoughts have creative power. Every thought you think is creating your future and changing you. Wow! Just meditate on that for a bit.

You think about whatever your focus is on. As you choose good thoughts, which have positive vibrations or energy, you attract more of the same. Good thoughts cause more good thoughts. This is known as the Law of Attraction. This law applies to everything you think, believe, act, intend, say, and the emotions you experience. Simply put, what you focus on is what you attract. What you attract is what you become.

Your emotions are an internal guidance system. When you experience positive emotions such as joy and happiness, you are vibrating in harmony with your goals and desires. Alternately, when you experience negative emotions such as fear, anger, nervousness, or anxiety, you are off track and vibrating at a lower frequency.

This is how the Law of Attraction works. You will attract what you are thinking and feeling. The more positive you feel, the more you attract positive circumstances. Likewise, the more negative you feel, the more you attract negative circumstances. You have the ability to elevate higher and higher or descend lower and lower.

Your emotions are gifts that enable you to see what your thought life is like. As such, they are always a measurement of what you will experience. Maintaining positive thinking is a vital step toward living a happy, abundant life. In order to continually have positive thoughts, you must intentionally choose your thought life. As you celebrate and focus on the good, you will attract more of it.

Understanding your thinking that leads to your thought patterns leads us to how your brain works. Thought patterns express themselves in areas of the brain that contain your subconscious and conscious mind.

Thought processes are formed through feelings, positive or negative, leading to the brain to establish pathways of thinking. Have you ever noticed that you may perform a sequence of actions as you awaken and prepare for your day sub-consciously? Perhaps you get out of bed, go to the kitchen and drink a glass of lemon water, then head to the shower. After you shower, you brush your teeth, get dressed, and then eat breakfast.

Your conscious mind is logical: it reasons, performs critical thinking, formulates plans; it is our will. Your subconscious mind never sleeps; it works 24 hours a day 7 days a week. This is where your beliefs, habits, emotions and intuition reside.

This example will clarify the difference: When you first learned to roller skate, all of your concentration was on maintaining your balance as you used the handrail to steady yourself, focusing on moving forward while remaining upright, and looking straight ahead so as not to bump into anyone. It required all your concentration. Once you skated for a period of time, you got onto the rink and no longer held the rail to steady yourself or focused on moving one foot forward at a time, instead you had a conversation with your friends and kept time to the music. It was fun.

Once you created cellular memory of skating, which your subconscious recalls, you no longer needed to concentrate on the act of skating; you just did it. In regard to your morning routine, completing these steps requires no thought; you do them as if you are on autopilot. While your day could progress with a number of other sequences, your brain has built pathways that created this routine. Therefore, if you change the pattern for a few days or weeks, your brain will create a new pathway.

In your brain, thoughts are electrical energy firing currents along a roadway. Your brain creates pathways based on your emotions that you think about. Some may have been created by fear, shame or distrust. As a child, they might have been necessary for your safety.

As previously learned, you may experience stress, tension, anxiety, depression, chaos and other negative feelings without even considering how they affect you emotionally and physically. These negative feelings ultimately lower your frequency and the body's electrical system. This weakens the body's ability to fight off infection, sickness and disease. Negative thinking can lead your mind into toxic thinking, which has a serious effect on your body.

Dr. Barry Gordon, a neurologist, states, "We are aware of a tiny fraction of the thinking that goes on in our minds, and we can control only a tiny part of our conscious thoughts. The vast majority of our thinking efforts goes on subconsciously. Only one or two of these thoughts are likely to breach into consciousness at a time. Slips of the tongue and accidental actions offer glimpses of our unfiltered subconscious mental life."[11]

Before you learn how you can change sub-conscious thoughts by changing your electrical signals, you need to understand how dangerous negative thinking is.

"If you want to find the secrets of the universe, think in terms of energy, frequency and vibration."
—Nikola Tesla

TOXIC THOUGHTS

Since you are usually not aware of the effects that your thoughts can have on your body's energy centers, then you probably haven't considered how seriously negative feelings can affect you. Strong feelings like stress, tension, anxiety, or depression have the ability to lower your frequency. Negative thinking will lead to toxic thinking, which may lead to sickness, disease and death.

Most people know that stress is your worst enemy, but did you know that stress is the direct result of toxic thinking? It has been shown to disrupt your sleep and weaken your digestive and immune systems. These physiological weaknesses eventually result in high internal toxicity, further weakening your resilience.

You need to ask yourself how many toxic thoughts you are permitting. It is actually pretty simple to conclude because those types of thoughts will trigger negative, unsettling emotions and result in a general feeling of discontent.

Toxic thoughts occupy mental "real estate" in your brain that are poisonous to you. They actually trigger the production of bio-chemicals within your body that results in stress on the physical level. Science tells us toxic thoughts are stored in your mind as well as in the cells of your body.

The longer negative thoughts are present, the more active they become, until they influence every decision, word and action that you make. Eventually, as I previously stated, your life falls into a cycle of failing and accepting our failures as your lot in life. The impact of toxic thinking and emotions may impact your physical body by:

- Developing a headache when you experience stress
- Increasing respiration and heart rate when you are frightened

- Upsetting digestion when you are angry
- Hampering your ability to live and enjoy life fully
- Inhibiting proper function of bodily systems
- Experiencing unexplained pain and illness
- Resulting in emotional imbalances
- Suppressing the immune system
- Lowering the frequency level of your body

By intentionally choosing to control your thoughts, you can change the course of your day and even your life. This involves removing all toxic emotions and thoughts from your mind and body. You can accomplish this process by the words that you speak.

"The happiness in your life depends upon the quality of your thoughts."
—Marcus Aurelius

THOUGHTS AND WORDS

Eventually your thinking process is going to lead to your brain sending those thoughts to your mouth. Words can be defined as sound or combination of sounds that have meaning and are spoken by a human being.[12]

Have you ever said something before you thought about it and wished you hadn't spoken? The words you spoke are a product of your thoughts. Every word you speak emits a negative or positive vibration. These vibrations are attracting the same energy that you are emitting.

In *The Law of Attraction*, author Michael J. Losier said: "Words are everywhere. We speak them, read them, and hear them in our head… the words we think and use generate the vibration we send out."[13]

When God created the earth, He used words. God, who is light, *spoke* our universe into existence. He could have thought the world into existence, but He probably wanted you to know how powerful your words are. The Bible tells you that we are children of God. He gave you the power to speak over your life. Proverbs 19:21 states that, "Death and life are in the power of the tongue."

Remember when you read the scripture that "as a man thinks so is he"? You are cementing that image with your mouth.

"A good man out of the good treasure of his heart brings forth good; and an evil man out of the evil treasure of his heart [a brings forth evil. For out of the abundance of the heart his mouth speaks."
—Luke 6:45

Here is the connection between your thoughts and your mouth: Out of your heart or mind (sub-conscious or conscious), your tongue speaks. Talking negatively comes from thinking negatively. Talking positively comes from positively thinking.

The words that we speak are instrumental in rebuilding new pathways for grace, trust, mercy and forgiveness. We build new pathways by refusing the old thoughts and deciding to think new thoughts.

In Romans 12:2, this process is called renewing the mind: *"And be not conformed to this world: but be ye transformed by the renewing of your mind, that ye may prove what [is] that good, and acceptable, and perfect, will of God."*

Has your day ever started with a stubbed toe as soon as you got out of bed? Did your day continue to spiral downward? It probably played out something like this: first, you couldn't find your car keys. Then you were late for work, and of course, you spilled your lunch on your new dress. Did your day keep spiraling? I bet it did, unless you intentionally took the time to renew your mind.

Knowing this sequence is important for you to understand how bad things happen to good people. Negative thinking leads to toxic thoughts. Toxic thoughts lead to spiritual, physical, and mental anguish that will lead to negative words. The words that you speak have the ability to create your environment with emotions, good or bad, that will be stored in every cell of your body.

Letting go of the old and putting on the new might take time, depending upon how long you used the old pathways. Speaking out loud with positive, powerful words has been identified by some as affirmations. Affirmations are empowering, deliberate words that you may use to upgrade your emotions and renew your mind.

By stating an affirmation, such as "I am a healthy, abundant, peaceful person" aloud, you begin the process of renewing your mind. As your belief about yourself becomes more and more positive, so do your emotions. Remember, your emotions have an impact on your physical, mental, and spiritual health because they control your thinking, behavior, and actions. These are the building blocks of your belief system.

You can spend your entire lifetime with beliefs that are untrue. At one time, people believed the world was flat, so they were afraid to travel too far for fear they would fall off the edge of the earth. To you and I that is laughable, but to those individuals it was truth.

According to Karol Truman in *Feelings Buried Alive Never Die*, feelings are perceived through thoughts. The thought process, or thinking, will lead to emotions. As you think, you act through talking. Say it long enough and you may produce strong feelings that will lead to your beliefs, whether true or false. Your reality is determined by your perception of your feelings and emotions, either positive or negative.[14]

Interestingly, much of your behavior is driven by your belief system, and for many, your belief systems match those of your parents. A person raised by an individual with a poverty mindset will likely grow up with that same poverty mindset. Changing your thoughts and words may give you an extra bonus of financial freedom.

It takes a lot of very intentional effort to look at yourself and identify the beliefs that are controlling your life. However, knowing your beliefs will give you a sound basis for emotional, spiritual, and physical action for change.

Now that you understand how detrimental negative emotions and toxic thoughts and words are to your body, you need to know how to change them. Before we learn how to clear negative emotions, toxic thinking and wrong belief system, we need to explore one more God-given tool to make the process of changing our lives easier.

SMELLS AND ESSENTIAL OILS

I am so thankful that God has made provision for us to maintain our health by creating plants and trees.

"Fruit trees of all kinds will grow along both sides of the river. The leaves of these trees will never turn brown and fall, and there will always be fruit on their branches. There will be a new crop every month, for they are watered by the river flowing from the Temple. The fruit will be for food and the leaves for healing." Ezekiel 47:12

Before you learn how to clear negative emotions from your body and belief systems from your mind, you need to explore the use of pure, therapeutic-grade essential oils. These precious oils are extracted from plants and trees in a very precise manner, so as to maintain their therapeutic properties.

In much the same manner that your body can experience a physical reaction to an emotion, aromas can invoke an emotional response. Can you associate a particular smell with a memory? Perhaps the wonderful smell of apple pie baking at home when you were a child evokes feelings of being loved and nurtured. When I was a young girl and smelled the pine Christmas tree and cinnamon bread baking, I felt happy and safe. My brain created a pathway that connects these scents to those emotions.

It is not hard to understand the connection between smell, your body and emotions. There is a pathway that takes smells into your brain. So when you experience a familiar smell, your brain is programmed to associate specific emotions to it. They can be positive or negative, depending on the events and personal experiences.

When you inhale a fragrance, the odor molecules travel up your nose into the limbic system of the brain. From studies conducted at New York Medical University, Dr. Ledoux and Dr. Hirsch discovered that the amygdala (a part of the limbic system) plays a major role in storing and releasing emotional traumas, and that aromas may exert a profound effect in triggering a response from the amygdala.[15]

Pure, therapeutic-grade essential oils have been known to be some of the oldest agents in history to have the ability to travel through our olfactory system. They find their way to the amygdala region of our brain just as any other smell. Science teaches us that smell stimulates our emotions first, and our rational brain second. The opposite occurs with our other four senses; stimulations of sight, sound, touch and taste all pass through our rational brain first before affecting the emotional brain. This is one of the reasons pure therapeutic essential oils are powerful in assisting the body to remain in balance or at homeostasis.

Dr. David Stewart explains so clearly in his book, *Healing Oils of the Bible*, how essential oils may bring your body into balance:

> "When an essential oil penetrates into the central brain, it makes it possible for us to access forgotten memories of emotions with which we need to deal. Stored emotions can make us sick. If they are stored in the stomach, you can have stomach ailments. If in the pancreas, you can have diabetes. … In such cases, some emotional trauma has been repressed and stored in cellular memory that blocks our natural ability to let love flow towards others and/or towards themselves. Hence, when essential oils trigger an emotionally upsetting memory, it gives us an opportunity to deal with that emotion and release it from our systems."[16]

While emotions are rarely considered a root source of physical symptoms, you can see from Dr. Stewart's explanation why they are a source of health for your body.

> "The spiritual dimension is the energetic basis of all life, because it is the energy of spirit which animates the physical framework. The unseen connection between the physical body and the subtle forces of spirit holds the key to understanding the inner relationship between matter and energy."[17]

Essential Oil Basics

- Pure essential oils are the volatile liquids distilled from plants.
- Pure essential oils are minute in molecular size, allowing them to penetrate the skin quickly.
- When inhaled, essential oils go directly to the limbic portion of the brain, where emotions are stored.
- The use of essential oils has been documented for thousands of years.
- Purity is crucial; approximately 2% of essential oils are actually pure.
- Pure essential oils contain numerous constituents.
- Citrus oils (except for Orange and Tangerine), Angelica, and Bergamot may cause photosensitivity to skin exposed to direct sunlight or UV rays within 24 hours after application.
- Avoid oils in the eyes, and do not pour oils in the ears.
- If essential oils cause any discomfort or irritation, they can be diluted by adding vegetable or fatty oils, also known as carrier oils. So have a bottle of carrier oil handy.
- Individuals with sensitivities should test a small amount of oil on an area, such as the inside of the upper arm, for 30 minutes prior to applying the oil to other areas.
- To ensure potency for many years, store essential oils in a cool, dark location, and keep the lids tightly closed.

How to Choose Essential Oils

Some of you reading this book may not know how to choose essential oils. Since the majority of the medical profession ignores medicines of our ancient culture, it is necessary to learn about them. First you should know that all oils are not equal to each other. When determining what oil company to purchase your oils, make sure you understand their "seed to seal" process:[18]

1. **Seed**: Seeds should come from plants with the highest possible levels of bioactive compounds for a given species.
2. **Cultivation**: The company selling oils should own farms and have co-op farms that are verified/audited for high standards for growing and cultivating the plants used for essential oils.
3. **Distillation**: Both ancient and modern techniques for steam extracting should be used for preserving the plants' precious constituents. Diverse methods, such as cold pressing and resin tapping, should be used for certain oils.
4. **Test**: You should NEVER use diluted, cut, or adulterated oils. Oils should be tested in the oil company's labs, as well as in third party facilities. Knowledge of the natural bioactive compounds in the species of plant that will produce the highest healing oil should be practiced by the company from which you buy your essential oils.
5. **Seal**: The company should bottle their own oils with a guarantee of "seed to seal" quality.

To some this may sound a little extreme, but you are not buying a pair of shoes. The quality of your oils will depend on the practices and belief system of the company from which you purchase your oils. Pure unadulterated that follow the seed to seal process will afford you peace of mind if you decide to take them internally. If the bottle says "external use only" or "not for internal use" or have any kind of warning, do not use!

How to Use Essential Oils

TOPICAL application provides a variety of options:

- The bottom of the feet is a great starting point
- Massage using a carrier oil
- Acupressure points
- Vita Flex Technique
- Auricular points
- Bath—add Epsom salts plus 3-10 drops of essential oil
- Warm Compress
- Pulse points as perfume or cologne
- Energy Centers / Chakras
- Raindrop Technique® (visit www.RaindropTraining.com for information on Raindrop Training Programs)
- Spritzer

AROMATIC application may be utilized in the following ways:

- Diffuser
- Drop the oil in the palm of the hand then rub the hands together, cup the hands directly over the mouth and nose, and inhale slowly
- Diffuser necklace
- Nasal inhaler
- Cotton ball or tissue

INTERNAL application options:

- Under the tongue
- In liquid, such as NingXia Red®
- Capsule
- Suppository
- Food or drink

Pure Therapeutic Essential oils can be added to a pure vegetable oil or other fatty oil, which works as a carrier, for more efficient use, especially when applying to a large area. When applying to infants, children, or those with sensitivities, dilution with a carrier oil is encouraged. Once children have been introduced to an essential oil, dilution may not be necessary.

CLEARING NEGATIVE EMOTIONS

As we have established, essential oils are wonderful tools to assist in the clearing process. They tend to bring about results at an astounding rate. When utilizing essential oils, it is a good idea to begin slowly, so as not to bring on detoxification too quickly. If at any time you feel overly emotional, reduce both the amount of oil you are using and the frequency of use. Once you begin to level off again, gradually increase your essential oil use.

It is certainly up to you how fast you want to detox. Whatever you decide to do, be sure that you have no fear of the process. The Bible says that, "God has not given us the spirit of fear, but power, love and a sound mind." (2 Timothy 1:7)

If you have completed a physical detox or cleanse at some point, think of an emotional detox in the same aspect, except with your focus shifted to emotions. Normally, when we do an emotional cleanse, the emotions we are detoxing become stronger, more dominant. The reason for this is that memories deeply stored in the body are coming to the surface as a result of the detoxing protocol. While this may be daunting, it is actually a positive indication that the detoxification is working.

Just as with a detoxification of your physical body, an emotional cleanse can be uncomfortable. You suppressed the negative feelings in the first place because they were uncomfortable at the time, and you either chose not to deal with them or felt you were not able to do so.

Before you get started, there are a few old thought processes that may need to be addressed. First and foremost, you must forgive yourself, which you may find more difficult than forgiving others. The truth is, everyone makes mistakes and deserves grace and mercy.

The second thing that you need to do is love yourself. Jesus said that you should love others as you love yourself. Some people have an issue with releasing negative emotions because they don't think they are worthy.

To summarize:

1. Do not fear the process.
2. Forgive yourself.
3. Love yourself.
4. Do not judge yourself or others.
5. Allow yourself grace.

Do not think that you can release every negative thought, every toxic emotion, and every hurtful event from your life during one emotional release. It took a lifetime to accumulate these emotions in your body; it may take several emotional detoxes before you feel totally free.

In every experience, no matter how painful or tragic, there is always a lesson. Train yourself to see the lesson. Learn from it and move forward a wiser individual.

God made you perfectly! Life, family, other people, and circumstances have changed you. But God gave you His plants, our *medicines*, to restore you to His original plan. Trust in Him.

"Trust in the Lord will all your heart, and lean not on your own understanding; In all your ways acknowledge Him, and He shall direct your paths." Proverbs 3:5-6

Allowing yourself a lot of grace to work through this process is essential. When you do, the rewards are plentiful and so worth the effort. Remember that YOU are worth it!

> **Some of the best lessons we ever learn are learned from past mistakes. The error of the past is the wisdom and success of the future.**
> ***—Dale Turner***

Tips for a successful emotional detox:

- Have a strong support system in place when you begin this process.
- Prepare yourself mentally.
- Clear your calendar so the detox is your primary focus.
- Take half your body weight in pounds, and drink that number of ounces of water daily.
- Spend time in prayer or meditation renewing your mind.
- Keep a daily journal.
- Visualize yourself healthy and happy.
- Forgive yourself and others.
- Be patient; allow yourself time to balance.
- If you feel out of control at any time, seek professional advice.

TECHNIQUES TO ENHANCE EMOTIONAL WORK

Let's explore the following complimentary techniques to enhance emotional work: Reflexology, Vita Flex, and Auricular Acupuncture. The addition of essential oils to these techniques synergizes the therapy, assisting to bring balance to the body.

Reflexology

Reflexology is a non-intrusive complementary health therapy. The art of reflexology is based on the theory that points on the feet, hands, lower legs, ears, and face correspond with different areas of the body.

Reflexology dates back more than 5,000 years to Ancient Egypt, China and India, but was not introduced to the Western world until approximately 1913 by Dr. William Fitzgerald. Known as the father of zone therapy, Dr. Fitzgerald spoke of the connection between the mind and body and was the first known doctor to chart the areas where pressure could be applied in order to improve ailment areas.[19]

Dr. Joe Shelby Riley, who was trained by Dr. Fitzgerald, further developed zone therapy by adding eight horizontal divisions to the zones of the feet and hands. His work is accurately considered the beginning of modern reflexology.

As it is known today, reflexes found on the feet and hands follow the anatomy of the body. Riley's work with reflexes and zones also included the hands and ears.

During the 1930s, Eunice D. Ingham worked for Dr. Riley and continued to refine and improve his work. From her first book, *Stories the Feet Can Tell* (1938), she was encouraged by Riley and others to take her work into the public sphere. Eunice's major contribution to working with reflexes was that alternating pressure stimulated healing rather than having a numbing effect as it was thought to prior to that point. [20]

The Mayo Clinic has reported the following benefits of receiving reflexology:

- promotes relaxation
- reduces pain
- assists with psychological symptoms such as anxiety and depression
- enhances sleep
- effective palliative care of individuals with cancer[17]

You may apply a drop or two of an essential oil(s) prior to performing reflexology.

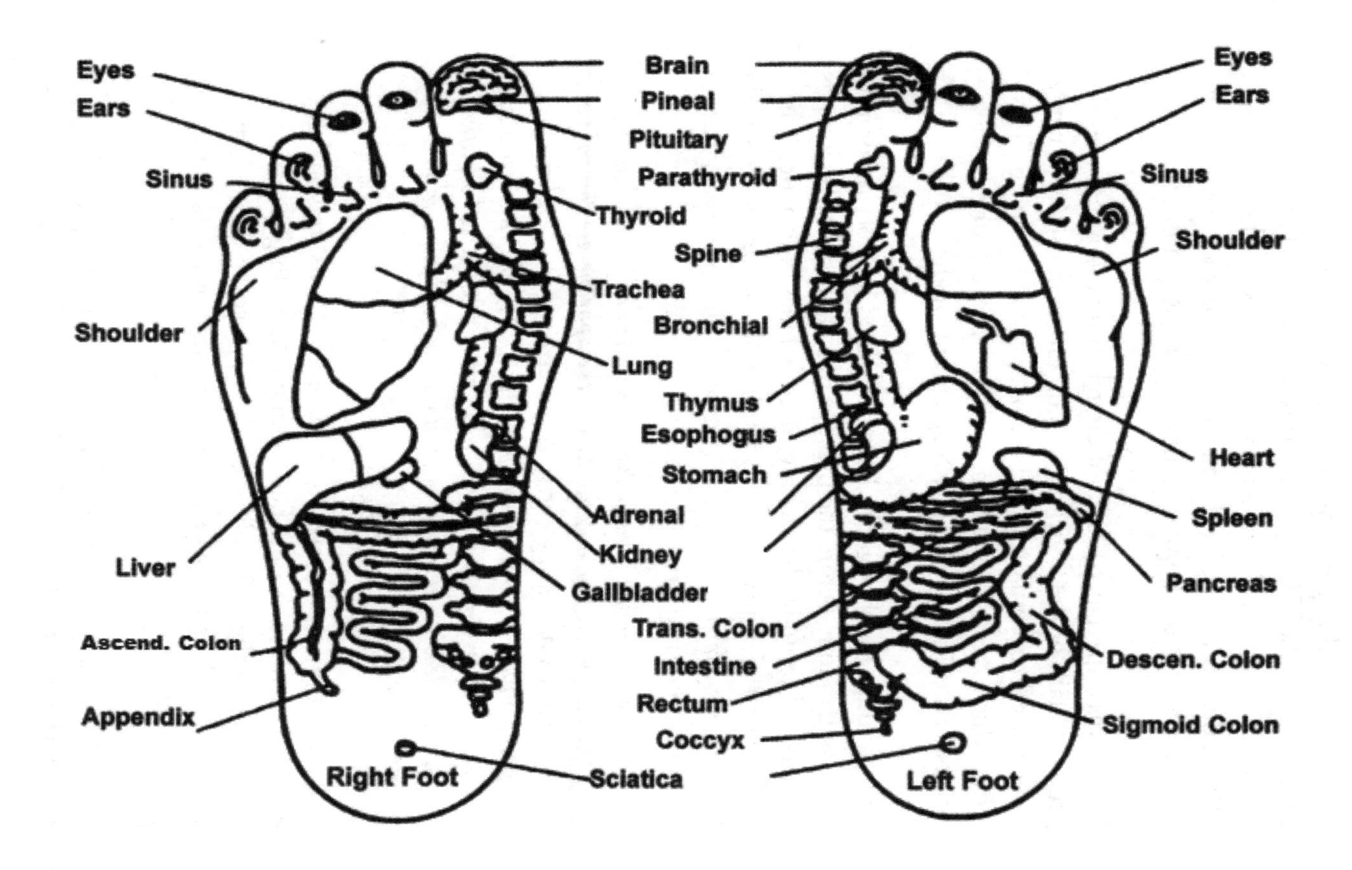
Eyes
Ears
Sinus
Shoulder
Liver
Ascend. Colon
Appendix
Right Foot
Brain
Pineal
Pituitary
Parathyroid
Thyroid
Spine
Trachea
Bronchial
Lung
Thymus
Esophogus
Stomach
Adrenal
Kidney
Gallbladder
Trans. Colon
Intestine
Rectum
Coccyx
Sciatica
Eyes
Ears
Sinus
Shoulder
Heart
Spleen
Pancreas
Descen. Colon
Sigmoid Colon
Left Foot

Vita Flex Technique

Vita flex is another technique that is used to help enhance emotional releases for the body. This technique is based on the touch of a person's fingers to create an electrical current or voltage that stimulates the frequency of the body. Increasing the frequency helps the body to fight off sickness and disease.

Vita flex is a specialized form of digital stimulation that uses the pads and nails of the fingers in a rolling motion to move energy (or electrical currents) through the body via reflex points. This term, which means "vitality through the reflexes," or control points, was coined vita flex by Stanley Burroughs.

This technique is thought to have originated in Tibet thousands of years ago, long before the practice of acupuncture. Burroughs refined and brought the technique from Tibet to America during the early 20th century. The original English text on vita flex is the book *Healing for the Age of Enlightenment* which Burroughs wrote and first published prior to 1950.

> *"Vita flex is based upon a complete system of internal body controls. When properly applied to the appropriate control points, a vibration of healing energy is released to heal, to relieve all pain, and to remove the symptoms as well as the causes of illness. This reflex system of controls encompasses the entire body and mind, releasing all kinds of tensions, congestions, and mal-adjustments."*[21]

You may apply a drop or two of an essential oil(s) to your chosen area and then use the vita flex technique of rolling your fingers, beginning on the pads rolling all the way over to the nail, three to six times. This will synergize the essential oils, creating a more powerful application.

*Detailed classes explaining how to do this technique can be found at www.careclasses.com.

The vita flex technique is effective at bringing balance to the sympathetic nervous system which controls the body's responses to a perceived threat and is responsible for the "fight or flight" response. Vita flex also benefits the parasympathetic nervous system, which maintains homeostasis, the body at rest, and the body's "rest and digest" function.[22]

Auricular Acupuncture

Auricular acupuncture is a diagnostic and treatment system based on normalizing the body's dysfunction by stimulating definite points on the ear. The improvement that follows is believed to be through the reticular formation, which is a network of neurons in the brainstem involved in consciousness, regulation of breathing, the transmission of sensory stimuli to higher brain centers, and the constantly shifting muscular activity that supports the body against gravity.

The modern version of auriculotherapy was first developed in 1957 by Dr. Paul Nogier, a French neurologist. Dr. Nogier's work demonstrated that the ear is actually a micro-map of the entire body with all body parts represented. Thus, all parts of the body can be evaluated and treated by means of the external ear.

Studies and experience have revealed auriculotherapy is effective in both the emotional and physical realms. For example, the very tip of the ear is connected to emotions you have surrounding your mother, (see picture) while the area just below that is connected to your emotions about your father. Along the outside edge of your ear down to the lobe are points connected to depression, feelings of being overwhelmed, and carrying the weight of the world.[23]

One single-blind clinical study published in PubMed evaluated the efficacy of auriculotherapy with and without a set protocol for reducing stress levels among nursing staff. It revealed that individualized auriculotherapy may be helpful in reducing the effects of stress.[24]

Another study of auricular acupuncture for primary insomnia was published in PubMed, indicating that it may effectively improve sleep quality.[25]

Refer to the ear chart on page 47, locate the emotion you desire to target, identify the associated area of the ear and apply a drop or two of an essential oil(s) suggested for that specific emotion as found on pages 48-56.

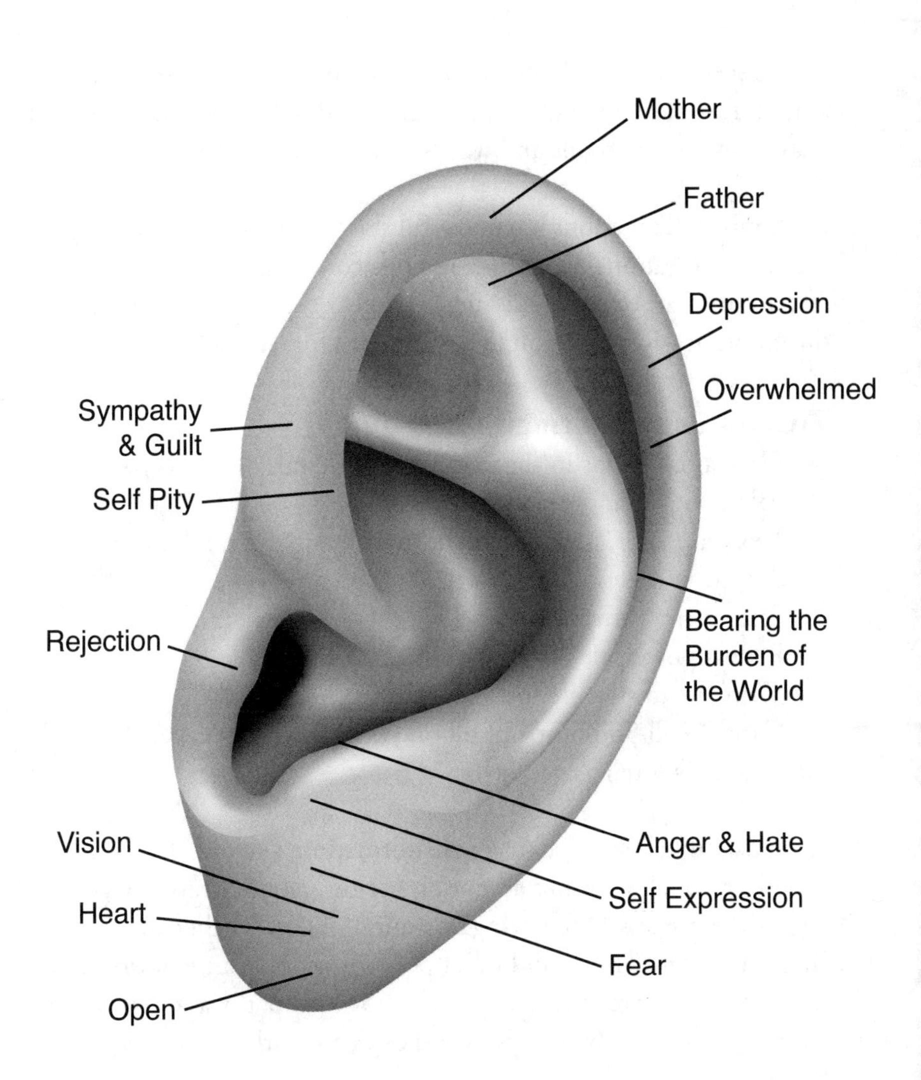
Mother
Father
Depression
Overwhelmed
Sympathy & Guilt
Self Pity
Bearing the Burden of the World
Rejection
Anger & Hate
Vision
Self Expression
Heart
Fear
Open

EMOTIONS, OILS AND AFFIRMATIONS

In this section, you will locate specific emotions (alphabetically) that you would like to clear. For each emotion, you will find choices for essential oils and words to use to accomplish this.

Remember affirmations are powerful statements. By making very specific affirmations, we take conscious control of our thoughts. The addition of essential oils aids to quickly release and change the emotions. Repeat as often as necessary for success!

Tips for using affirmations and oils

- Place a few drops in the palm of your hand, then rub your palms together.
- Next cup your hand over your mouth and nose, inhaling deeply.
- State your affirmation aloud.
- Repeat powerful, short statements 3 times.
- Write down statements on a 3x5 card.
- Carry small 5ml bottle of oil on you or in a purse.
- Repeat as often as necessary.

As an example, when we make an affirmation, such as "I choose to be a loving and accepting person" aloud, hearing it begins the process of renewing our mind. As your belief about yourself becomes more and more positive, so do your emotions. Remember you are taking steps to remove old pathways, by creating new brain pathways as you explored earlier in the book.

ABANDONMENT

Acceptance™, Bergamot, Christmas Spirit™, Forgiveness™, Valor®.

I am cherished. I am cared for. I am precious.

ABUNDANCE
Abundance™, Oola® Finance™, Acceptance™, Ginger, Harmony™, Gathering™, Rose.

I am abundant. I have everything I need. I am complete.

ACCEPTANCE
Acceptance™, Citrus Fresh™, Oola® Grow™, Sacred Mountain™, Surrender™, Transformation™.

I am secure. I am appreciated. I am accepted.

ANGER
Bergamot, Cedarwood, Christmas Spirit™, Forgiveness™, Joy™, Lavender, Myrrh, Orange, Peace & Calming®, Release™, Roman Chamomile, Rose, Surrender™, Tranquil, Trauma Life™, Valor®, Ylang Ylang.

I am love. I am calm. I am forgiveness.

BRAVERY
Believe™, Clarity™, Fennel, Live with Passion™, Magnify Your Purpose™, Oola® Faith™, Valor®.

I am fearless. I am brave. I am confident.

CALMNESS
Cedarwood, Gathering™, Harmony™, Lavender, Orange, Peace & Calming®, Roman Chamomile, Valerian, Ylang Ylang.

I am calm. I am peaceful. I have faith.

CLARITY
Awaken™, Brain Power™, Cedarwood, Clarity™, Frankincense, Present Time™, Rosemary, Transformation™.

I am clear-headed. I understand. I know.

CONFIDENCE
Build Your Dream™, Envision™, Grounding™, Highest Potential™, Inspiration™, Idaho Blue Spruce, Jasmine, Shutran™, Transformation™, Valor®.

I am confident. I am secure. I trust myself.

CONFUSION
Awaken™, Brain Power™, Cedarwood, Clarity™, Cypress, Frankincense, Gathering™, Grounding™, Harmony™, Juniper, Marjoram, Peppermint, Present Time™, Sandalwood, Transformation™, Valor®.

I comprehend. I understand. I have clarity.

DESPERATION
Acceptance™, Believe™, Clary Sage, Geranium, Gratitude™, Hope™, Lemon, Joy™, Oola® Fun™, Motivation™, Peppermint, Rosemary, Transformation™, Valor®, Ylang Ylang.

I am confident. I am trusting. I am composed.

DISCOURAGEMENT
Bergamot, Build Your Dream™, Cedarwood, Citrus Fresh™, Dream Catcher™, Frankincense, Geranium, Hope™, Inspiration™, Joy™, Juniper, Lemon, Live With Passion™, Juniper, Sandalwood, Valor®, Vetiver.

I am encouraged. I am excited. I am eager.

FEAR
Acceptance™, Bergamot, Clary Sage, Gentle Baby™, Gratitude™, Harmony™, Highest Potential™, Hope™, Inner Child™, Into the Future™, Joy™, Myrrh, Release™, Roman Chamomile, Rose, SARA™, Shutran™, Stress Away™, Valor®, White Angelica™.

I trust. I am confident. I am resolute.

FRUSTRATION
Acceptance™, Clary Sage, Frankincense, Ginger, Gathering™, Harmony™, Hope™, Humility™, Lavender, Lemon, Oola® Balance™, Orange, Peppermint, Present Time™, Roman Chamomile, Surrender™, 3 Wise Men™, Valor®.

I am peaceful. I am relaxed. I am confident.

GRATITUDE
Believe™, Gratitude™, Idaho Balsam Fir, Oola® Faith™, Forgiveness™, Humility™, Rose, Sacred Mountain™, White Angelica™.

I am thankful. I am grateful. I am blessed.

GRIEF
Bergamot, Cedarwood, Clary Sage, Forgiveness™, Harmony™, Hope™, Inner Child™, Into the Future™, Joy™, Juniper, Lavender, Magnify Your Purpose™, Present Time™, Oola® Faith™, Release™, Transformation™, White Angelica™.

I am comforted. I am consoled. I am soothed.

GUILT
Acceptance™, Cypress, Forgiveness™, Frankincense, Gathering™, Geranium, Gratitude™, Harmony™, Inspiration™, Inner Child™, Lemon, Peace & Calming®, Present Time™, Release™, Rose, Thyme, Valor®, White Angelica™.

I am forgiven. I am love. I have peace of mind.

HARMONY
Acceptance™, Believe™, Geranium, Harmony™, Inspiration™, Live with Passion™, Oola® Family™, Oola® Field™, Roman Chamomile, Surrender™, White Angelica™, Ylang Ylang, 3 Wise Men™.

I am happy. I am at peace. I am content.

HOPELESSNESS

Christmas Spirit™, Dream Catcher™, Egyptian Gold™, Evergreen Essence™, Gathering™, Hope™, Inspiration™, Joy™, Motivation™, Transformation™, White Angelica™.

I trust. I have faith. I have hope.

INSPIRATION

Believe™, Cedarwood, Clarity™, Gratitude™, Highest Potential™, Inspiration™, Into the Future™, Live with Passion™, Motivation™, Rosemary, Valor®.

I am enthusiastic. I am inspired. I can do it.

INTIMIDATION

Acceptance™, Believe™, Grounding™, Citrus Fresh™, Ginger, Live with Passion™, Magnify Your Purpose™, Transformation™, Valor®.

I am confident. I am assured. I am at ease.

INSPIRATION

Australian Blue™, Clarity™, Envision™, Frankincense, Highest Potential™, Inspiration™, Oola® Faith™, Peppermint, Rosemary, Sacred Mountain™, 3 Wise Men™.

I am inspired. I am motivated. I can.

JEALOUSY

Bergamot, Frankincense, Forgiveness™, Harmony™, Humility™, Joy™, Lemon, Marjoram, Orange, Rose, Rosemary, Sacred Mountain™, Thyme, Valor®, White Angelica™, Ylang Ylang.

I am love. I am harmonious. I am accepting.

JOY

Abundance™, Bergamot, Build Your Dream™, Christmas Spirit™, Citrus Fresh™, Evergreen Essence™, Gratitude™, Joy™, Live with Passion™, Magnify Your Purpose™, Oola® Fun™, Sacred Mountain™, Valor®.

I am joyful. I am cheerful. I am at peace.

LONELINESS
Acceptance™, Believe™, Bergamot, Forgiveness™, Roman Chamomile, Shutran™, Trauma Life™, Valor®, White Angelica™.

I love and accept myself. I am secure. I am connected.

LOVE
Forgiveness™, Joy™, Juniper, Lady Sclareol™, Lavender, Oola® Family™, Rose, Sensation™, Ylang Ylang.

I am loving. I am forgiving I am gracious.

MELANCHOLY
Acceptance™, Believe™, Inspiration™, Joy™, Oola® Fun™, Orange, Transformation™, 3 Wise Men™, Valor®.

I am happy. I am cheerful. I am delighted.

MOTIVATION
Envision™, Magnify Your Purpose™, Oola® Field™, Motivation™, Live with Passion™.

I move forward. I am motivated. I am successful.

NEGATIVITY
Dream Catcher™, Forgiveness™, Grapefruit, Inspiration™, Oola® Fun™, Palo Santo, Sacred Mountain™, Sandalwood, Transformation™.

I am positive. I am cheerful. I am happy.

NERVOUSNESS
Cedarwood, Frankincense, Jasmine, Marjoram, Oola® Balance™, Orange, Peace & Calming®, Petitgrain, Stress Away™, Surrender™, Valerian, Vetiver.

I am confident. I am peaceful. I am calm.

OBSESSIVENESS
Acceptance™, Awaken™, Clary Sage, Cypress, Forgiveness™, Geranium, Helichrysum, Humility™, Inner Child™, Joy™, Lavender, Live with Passion™, Motivation™, Oola® Grow™, Present Time™, Rose, Sacred Mountain™, Sandalwood, Valor®, Ylang Ylang.

I redirect my thinking. I am relaxed. I accept.

PANIC
Acceptance™, Believe™, Bergamot, Frankincense, Gathering™, Harmony™, Lavender, Marjoram, Myrrh, Peace & Calming®, Roman Chamomile, Rosemary, Sandalwood, Valor®, White Angelica™, Ylang Ylang.

I am trusting. I am fearless. I am peaceful.

PRIDE
Acceptance™, Clarity™, Frankincense, Grounding™, Gratitude™, Humility™, Oola® Balance™, Peppermint.

I am teachable. I am modest. I am humble.

RECKLESSNESS
Awaken™, Brain Power™, Common Sense™, Gathering™, Grounding™, Inspiration™, Peppermint.

I am thoughtful. I am attentive. I am careful.

REJECTION
Acceptance™, Forgiveness™, Grounding™, Inner Child™, Joy™, Oola® Family™, Present Time™, Release™, Sacred Mountain™, Transformation™.

I am loved. I am accepted. I am favored.

RESENTMENT
Forgiveness™, Harmony™, Humility™, Jasmine, Joy™, Release™, Rose, Surrender™, White Angelica™.

I love unconditionally. I choose to forgive. I am at peace.

RESILIENCE
Acceptance™, Into the Future™, Live with Passion™, Magnify Your Purpose™, Motivation™, Sacred Mountain™.

I am steadfast. I am moving forward. I am strong.

SHAME
Acceptance™, Forgiveness™, Hope™, Joy™, Oola® Grow™, Release™, SARA™, Transformation™, Trauma Life™, Valor®.

I am worthy. I am admirable. I am valued.

SHYNESS
Believe™, Envision™, Highest Potential™, Inspiration™, Live with Passion™, Magnify Your Purpose™, Peppermint, Rosemary, Valor®.

I am friendly. I am gregarious. I am assertive.

STRESS
Bergamot, Evergreen Essence™, Gentle Baby™, Joy™, Lavender, Peace & Calming®, RutaVaLa, Stress Away™, Surrender™, Tranquil™, Trauma Life™.

I am flowing with life. I am relaxed. I am peaceful.

TENSION
Bergamot, Cedarwood, Harmony™, Oola® Faith™, Peace & Calming®, RutaVaLa, Stress Away™, Tranquil™, Valerian.

I am fearless. Life is effortless. I am restful.

TERROR
Grounding™, Hope™, Joy™, Peace & Calming®, Release™, RutaVaLa, Sacred Mountain™, SARA™, Transformation™, Vetiver.

I am protected. I trust. I have faith.

TRAUMA
Acceptance™, Australian Blue™, Peace & Calming®, Release™, SARA™, Tranquil™, Trauma Life™, 3 Wise Men™, Valor®.

I am peaceful. I am accepting. I am safe.

UNFORGIVENESS

Acceptance™, Forgiveness™, Oola® Faith™, 3 Wise Men™, Transformation™, Valor®, White Angelica™.

I choose to forgive. I accept. I love.

WEARINESS

Brain Power™, Dream Catcher™, En-R-Gee™, Gratitude™, Highest Potential™, Magnify Your Purpose™, Orange, Peppermint, Transformation™.

I am vibrant. I am energetic. I am strong.

WORRY

Bergamot, Envision™, Evergreen Essence™, Oola® Faith™, Release™, Ylang Ylang.

I trust. I am steadfast. I have faith.

Unexpressed emotions never die. They are buried alive and will come forth later in uglier ways.
—*Sigmund Freud*

BALANCING ENERGY CENTERS

As you learned earlier, there are seven Chakra or energy centers located on your body. Let's explore each energy center and the oils that are known to help balance and or release the negative energy that may be blocking them.

1. **Root**—Located at the base of the spine.
   Represents our foundation and feeling of being grounded and secure.
   Affirmation: *I exist.*
   Balancing Oils: Cedarwood, Jasmine, Clove, Galbanum, Vetiver

2. **Sacral**—Located in the lower abdomen, just below navel.
   Our center for creating relationships and ability to accept others and new experiences.
   Affirmation: *I desire.*
   Balancing Oils: Bergamot, Rose, Sandalwood, Ylang Ylang

3. **Solar Plexus**—Located in the upper abdomen, center of stomach.
   Represents our personal power.
   Affirmation: *I control.*
   Balancing Oils: Lemon, Lavender, Ginger, Rosemary

4. **Heart**—Located over the heart, center of chest.
   Represents our ability to love.
   Affirmation: *I love.*
   Balancing Oils: Lavender, Rose, Marjoram, Jasmine

5. **Throat**—Located at the throat, at base of neck.
   Represents our self expression and creativity.
   Affirmation: *I express.*
   Balancing Oils: Frankincense, Sage, Peppermint, Lavender, Eucalyptus Globulus

6. **Third Eye**—Located in the center of the forehead.
   Represents the seat of intuition and decision making.
   Affirmation: *I am the witness.*
   Balancing Oils: Frankincense, Jasmine, Spearmint, Geranium, Palo Santo

7. **Crown**—Located at the top of the head.
   Represents enlightenment, the highest level of consciousness.
   Affirmation: *I am that I am.*
   Balancing Oils: Rose, Idaho Blue Spruce, Jasmine, Cedarwood

> **Thinking positive thoughts will always empower you! Do it enough and it will change your life!**
> ***—Timothy Pina***

EMOTIONAL CLEARING TECHNIQUE

Step #1
Write 10 things you are grateful for in your Gratitude Journal. An attitude of gratitude is essential to achieve emotional balance. Being grateful is an intentional choice, and the more you practice it, the easier it is to find the good in every situation.

Step #2
Choose the emotion you desire to clear and the related affirmation(s).

Step #3
Set your intention on becoming emotionally balanced.

Step #4
Balance the energy of the body with Valor®, Grounding™ or Lavender by applying 4 drops to the top of the shoulders and bottom of feet. Then cup your hands over your mouth and nose and take 5 deep breaths.

Step #5
Drop 3 drops of Release™, Ylang Ylang or Trauma Life™ into the palm of your non-dominant hand, activate by swirling the oil in clockwise circles with your dominant hand. Next, apply the oil in 3 clockwise rotations around the navel, repeating 3 times "I choose to release all negative emotions and receive that which is positive and uplifting to me." Then, cup your hands over your mouth and nose and take 5 deep breaths.

Step #6
Apply a drop of Frankincense or Clarity™ to each temple and the brain stem at the base of the skull.

Step #7
With your left forefinger, apply 1 drop of Idaho Blue Spruce to the top of your right foot between the big toe and second toe. While holding your finger on your foot, apply 1 drop of Idaho Blue Spruce to the middle of your forehead at the hairline with your right forefinger. Hold your fingers in place for 3 minutes as you say your chosen affirmation aloud 10 times.

Step #8
Using an oil or blend suggested for the specific emotion you are releasing, apply 3 drops to the center of your chest. Then, lightly tap 6 sets of 3 taps on your chest with the fingertips of your right hand.

Step #9
Apply 1 drop of Idaho Blue Spruce or Frankincense to the base of the skull with your fingertip, holding your finger at this point as you state your affirmation 3 times.

Step #10
Apply 1 drop of Idaho Blue Spruce or Frankincense just above each eyebrow with the fingertips of your forefingers, holding your fingers at this point as you state your affirmation 3 times.

Repeat these 10 steps twice daily for 30 days.

Oh, Happy Day

Step #1

Balance the energy of the body with Valor®, Grounding™, or Lavender by applying 4 drops to the top of the shoulders and bottom of feet. Then cup your hands over your mouth and nose and take 5 deep breaths.

Step #2

Apply 2 drops of Abundance™ or Patchouli on your ears, including the lobes and rim, while stating these affirmations 3 times each:

I have an abundant life.
I am healthy.
I am grateful.

Step #3

Apply 2 drops of Palo Santo or Highest Potential™ to the Third Eye chakra (center of your forehead). Then cup your hands over your mouth and nose and breathe deeply 3 times.

Step #4

Apply 3 drops of Harmony™ or Lavender in 3 clockwise rotations over the Solar Plexus chakra (upper abdomen, center of stomach). Then cup your hands over your mouth and nose and breathe deeply 3 times.

Step #5

Apply 3 drops of Bergamot or Joy™ over the Heart chakra (over the heart, center of chest). Then cup your hands over your mouth and nose and breathe deeply 3 times.

Step #6

Be a blessing to as many people as possible today.

Mix It Up

These are some of my favorite blends. You carry your personal diffuser with you everywhere you go. To use it, drop your oil blend into the palm of your hands, rub them together, cup your hands over your mouth and nose, and breathe deeply.

Stage Fright

Elemi—20 drops
Wintergreen—20 drops
Petitgrain—20 drops
Lavender—20 drops
Peppermint—20 drops
Frankincense—1 drop
Myrrh—1 drop

Apply to temples and brain stem, and inhale or diffuse.

Elation

Bergamot—20 drops
Ylang Ylang—20 drops
Tangerine—15 drops
Frankincense—1 drop
Myrrh—1 drop

Apply to pulse points, over heart, and inhale directly.

Silent Night

Orange—20 drops
Lavender—15 drops
Cedarwood—15 drops
Geranium—10 drops
Vetiver—3 drops

Apply to big toes, bottom of feet and back of neck, and diffuse.

Bully Buster

Bergamot—15 drops
Cypress—15 drops
Marjoram—10 drops
Orange—10 drops
Frankincense—1 drop
Myrrh—1 drop

Apply to top of shoulders, on the ears, and back of neck, and inhale.

Apply to pulse points and over heart, and inhale.

Yes I Can

Cedarwood—15 drops
Grapefruit—15 drops
Copaiba—10 drops
Lavender—10 drops
Rosemary—7 drops

Apply to top of shoulders, back of neck, bottom of feet and on the ears, and inhale or diffuse.

Momma's Secret

Grapefruit—20 drops
Patchouli—20 drops
Ylang Ylang—20 drops
Frankincense—1 drop
Myrrh—1 drop

Apply to pulse points and over the heart, and inhale or diffuse.

Paradigm Shift

Idaho Blue Spruce—15 drops
Ylang Ylang—15 drops
Idaho Balsam Fir—10 drops

Apply to brainstem, temples, behind the ears and big toes, and inhale or diffuse.

Peace Be Still

Clary Sage—15 drops
Lavender—15 drops
Orange—15 drops
Rosemary—9 drops
Frankincense—1 drop
Myrrh—1 drop

Apply to bottom of feet, over the heart and behind the ears, and inhale or diffuse.

Revelation

Cardamom—15 drops
Rosemary—10 drops
Basil—10 drops
Jasmine—8 drops
Ylang Ylang—6 drops
Frankincense—1 drop
Myrrh—1 drop

Apply to brainstem, temples, behind the ears and big toes, and inhale or diffuse.

You can create your own personal roll-on by topping off your bottle with fractionated coconut oil and adding a roller top.

EMOTIONAL QUESTIONNAIRES

If you're like most people, delving into your emotional realm can seem daunting. The following questionnaires provide excellent recommendations for helping to deal with a wide range of toxic emotions.

Simply check off or mark the feelings that apply to you. As you proceed through it, you may want to make a note of the oils that would be beneficial. ***One or more of these oils may be selected.*** Once you complete a few questionnaires, you will have a relatively good idea of what emotions you need to start working on and which oils you should gather.

Remember, by taking one step at a time, one day at a time, you will reach your goal of being emotionally healthy. The only way to fail is to not take that first step or to quit.

**Special thanks to Dr. Jay P. Vanden Heuval, Ph.D., IMD., DHS. for allowing the use of his questionnaires. To maintain FDA compliance, I have made some minor adjustments to the questionnaires.*

Emotional Questionnaire #1

- ❑ Are you compulsive, or do you have impulses to do things obsessively?
- ❑ Do you lack confidence in yourself?
- ❑ Do you expect failure?
- ❑ Do you feel inferior, or do you feel that others are more capable and qualified than you are?

Choose Bergamot

- Compulsive and/or obsessive behavior
- Tension
- Sadness
- Nervousness
- Lack of self-confidence

Emotional Questionnaire #2

- ❑ Do you frequently burst into tears or react in a highly emotional way to life's situations?
- ❑ Do you feel a lot of tension or congestion in your stomach or solar plexus, as though feelings are stored there?
- ❑ Do you believe you need to have more serenity in life?
- ❑ Do you fluctuate between emotional moods?
- ❑ Do you lack stamina?

Choose Roman Chamomile

- Darkness
- Tension
- Stress
- Anger
- Sleeplessness
- Hyperactivity
- Learning problems
- Moodiness
- Daydreaming
- Impatience

Emotional Questionnaire #3

- ❑ Do you anger easily?
- ❑ Are daily activities sometimes confusing?
- ❑ Are you easily irritated?

Choose Cinnamon Bark

- Tension
- Lack of inner self
- Lethargy
- Negative energy

Emotional Questionnaire #4

- ❑ Do you need to develop more objectivity and perspective about recent life events that trouble or perplex you?
- ❑ Does your life seem more accidental than purposeful, making it hard to have much insight into, or acceptance of, the people and events surrounding you?
- ❑ Are you in an elder phase of life, wanting to gather wisdom and reflect on the meaning of your experience?
- ❑ Do you have concern about aging?

Choose Clary Sage

- Aging (fear of)
- Immaturity
- Change or transitions
- Finding purpose
- Drawing wisdom from experience
- Ill-fated or undeserved feeling

Emotional Questionnaire #5

- ❑ Do you have difficulty with short-term memory?
- ❑ Do you feel out of touch with your intuition?
- ❑ Do you feel your emotions cloud your perception?
- ❑ Do you have a sense of detachment from the world?

Choose Clove

- Memory
- "Seeing" clearly
- Nervousness

Emotional Questionnaire #6

- ❑ Do you feel like you are being choked?
- ❑ Do you feel like you have something to say but are not saying it or expressing it?
- ❑ Do you have trouble accepting life as it is?
- ❑ Do you feel separate, resulting in a reduction of energy?

Choose Eucalyptus Globulus

- Constraint
- Loneliness
- Trouble accepting life

Emotional Questionnaire #7

- ❑ Do you suffer from unknown fears?
- ❑ Do you feel unsafe and insecure?
- ❑ Do you find it difficult to concentrate?
- ❑ Do you feel like the world is crashing in on you?
- ❑ Could you benefit from an infusion of faith?

Choose Frankincense

- Fear
- Uncertainty
- Poor concentration
- Insecurity
- Lack of self-confidence
- Nervousness
- Hyperventilation
- Hyperactivity

Emotional Questionnaire #8

- ❑ Do you hold grudges or refuse to let go of past hurts?
- ❑ Do you come on strong or seem overbearing to others, even though you are just trying to convey confidence?
- ❑ Do you feel overly tense or anxious?
- ❑ Do you suffer from mood swings?

Choose Geranium

- Overexcitement
- Nervousness
- Mood swings
- Weakness
- Nervous Tension
- PMS
- Sadness
- Letting go of past hurts

Emotional Questionnaire #9

- ❑ Do you have many plans or intentions that never seem to materialize?
- ❑ Do you brood, think about, or reflect, rather than plan and execute?
- ❑ Do you feel sluggish?
- ❑ Did you have a difficult childhood?

Choose Grapefruit

- Mood swings
- A sense of drowning in life
- Inner child issues
- Unresolved trauma from childhood

Emotional Questionnaire #10

- ❑ Are you in a state of crisis or emergency?
- ❑ Are you having trouble letting go of "stuck" emotions and hurts from the past?
- ❑ Is change difficult?
- ❑ Do you feel emotionally exhausted or disoriented?

Choose Helichrysum

- Shock
- Pain
- Trauma
- Helps remove stubborn emotions of jealousy, anger, and bitterness
- Great for the nerves
- Can be used for heavy metal detox
- Similar to Distress Remedy Homeopathic

Emotional Questionnaire #11

- ❑ Do you replace your daily life with fantasy?
- ❑ Do you need constant motivation to complete a task?
- ❑ Do you wish you had a better sense of well-being?

Choose Jasmine

- Impotence
- Grief
- Heartbreak
- Anger
- Sadness (including postpartum)
- Finding life's purpose

Emotional Questionnaire #12

- ❑ Would you describe yourself as strung out, nervous, or hyperactive?
- ❑ Do you have difficulty sleeping, or are you restless?
- ❑ Do you have difficulty concentrating when praying or meditating?
- ❑ Do you suffer from a chattering mind with no clear, calm, and concise thoughts?
- ❑ Is your life out of balance?

Choose Lavender

- Emotional blocks
- Stress
- For sensitive people
- Argumentative individuals
- Meditation
- Universal oil that relaxes and stimulates

Emotional Questionnaire #13

- ❏ Do your relationships seem toxic?
- ❏ Are you tense, or do you have unresolved conflict?
- ❏ Do you have lack of inner life?
- ❏ Do you describe yourself as being "out of it"?
- ❏ Do you tend to feel that everything is unclean?

Choose Lemon

- Issues of self
- Tiredness
- Lethargic
- Universal emotional balancer
- Feelings of impurity
- Nervousness

Emotional Questionnaire #14

- ❏ Do you suffer from everyday fears?
- ❏ Are you overworked?
- ❏ Do many people comment you don't seem happy?

Choose Orange

- Sadness
- Stress

Emotional Questionnaire #15

- ❑ Do you need a sense of comfort?
- ❑ Are you having difficulty getting over losing someone in any way?
- ❑ Are you sensitive, or impatient?
- ❑ Do you feel melancholy?

Choose Marjoram

- Heavy sighing
- Loneliness
- Rejection
- Sleeplessness
- Grief
- Tension
- Inappropriate sexual behavior/desire

Emotional Questionnaire #16

- ❑ Do you have trouble exercising patience?
- ❑ Is there a tendency to self-destruct?
- ❑ Do simple things irritate you?
- ❑ Do you suffer from a loss of stability?

Choose Myrrh

- Hyperactivity
- Stress
- Lack of inspiration

Emotional Questionnaire #17

- ❑ Do you have trouble making decisions?
- ❑ Do you anger easily?
- ❑ Do you often think, "What's the use"?
- ❑ Do you have general anxiety or fears?

Choose Neroli

- Sadness
- Nervousness
- Fear
- Sexual problems
- Tension (upset for no reason)
- Low libido
- Lack of self-confidence

Emotional Questionnaire #18

- ❑ Do you have trouble looking into a mirror and honestly saying "(*Your Name*), I love you?"
- ❑ Do you have difficulty seeing yourself as a unique individual?
- ❑ Do you feel your life is painful?

Choose Oregano

- Gives synergy to other oils for use in blends
- Pain
- Issues of self-esteem

Emotional Questionnaire #19

- ❑ Do you always need to be right?
- ❑ Do you have difficulty with decisions?
- ❑ Do you suffer from apathy or indifference?

Choose Patchouli

- Nervousness
- Stress
- Trapped emotional energy

Emotional Questionnaire #20

- ❑ Do you lack energy or stimulation?
- ❑ Do you find it hard to get motivated?
- ❑ Do you find it hard to get through the day?
- ❑ Do you have trouble being creative?

Choose Peppermint

- Sleeplessness
- Laziness
- Lethargy
- Sluggishness
- Mental cloudiness
- Low energy
- Poor concentration
- Good for students
- Helps with digestion of the body *and* the mind

Emotional Questionnaire #21

- ❑ Is it hard to find direction?
- ❑ Do you have harsh expectations of yourself?
- ❑ Is it hard to let go of past mistakes or failures?

Choose Pine

- Pity
- Guilt
- Blame
- Exhaustion
- Self-criticism

Emotional Questionnaire #22

- ❑ Is your heart heavy or sad?
- ❑ Do you lack comfort?
- ❑ Do you need to develop greater courage to confront rather than retreat?

Choose Rose

- Shame
- Sadness
- Grief
- Irritability
- Shyness
- **Inspires:** Joy, Love, Confidence, Love of Self, Inspiration, Renewal, Independence

Emotional Questionnaire #23

- ❑ Is there a side of you that needs more attention or understanding?
- ❑ Do you tell "white lies," or are you living a lie?
- ❑ Do you have trouble accepting your spiritual side, or do you question it?
- ❑ Do you see the world as pieces and parts rather than a meaningful whole?
- ❑ Are you forgetful, or are your extremities cold?

Choose Rosemary

- Confusion
- Exhaustion
- Bitterness
- Nightmares

- **Inspires:** Wisdom, Truth, Peace, Meditation, Creativity

Emotional Questionnaire #24

- ❑ Does life seem overly chaotic?
- ❑ Do you have trouble organizing your life?
- ❑ Do you suffer from a chattering mind or where daily activities and worries are constantly thought about? *(Obsessive compulsive)*

Choose Sandalwood

- Hyperactivity
- Negative programming

- Enhances meditation and prayer

Emotional Questionnaire #25

- ❑ Do you often deny your own needs?
- ❑ Do you care more about everyone else instead of spending time on yourself?

Choose Tea Tree

- Builds emotional strength

Emotional Questionnaire #26

- ❑ Do you spend time trying to understand the meaning of life?
- ❑ Do you feel like there is not enough time in your life to do everything you want to do?
- ❑ Do you feel that it's not fair that we age?

Choose Thyme

- Issues of time and trying to beat the clock
- Speeds healing of tissues
- **Builds:** Strength, Courage, Longevity, Concentration

Emotional Questionnaire #27

- ❑ Do you wear a mask of cheerfulness while you feel different on the inside?
- ❑ Do you judge before you act, & are you even aware of it?
- ❑ Do you ever have difficulty really "hearing" what others are saying?
- ❑ Do you have difficulty with imperfection, either in yourself, or others?
- ❑ Do life's unfolding events often irritate you?

Choose Ylang Ylang

- Hyperventilation
- Shock
- Stress
- Nervousness
- Anger
- Bitterness
- Sadness
- Lack of interest
- Jealousy

FINAL WORDS FROM THE AUTHOR

I trust you have enjoyed experiencing the profound effect of essential oils in clearing and detoxing the body of negative emotions. Bear in mind we are all uniquely created and will therefore have distinct experiences.

As long as we are on this earth we will have experiences, emotions and thoughts that will result in the necessity of repeating these techniques. Depending on the individual, some emotions are buried deeper than others and will require more attention to fully clear them. Please allow yourself the grace and time to accomplish this. You will be delighted that you did!

Continue to be intentionally grateful, visualizing yourself happy, healthy and emotionally free. Please share your successes with others that they may experience the same.

I challenge you to be a World Changer!

2 Corinthians 9:6-8—But this [I say], He which soweth sparingly shall reap also sparingly; and he which soweth bountifully shall reap also bountifully.

REFERENCE LIST

1 Dictionary.com, "Definition of emotion," <http://www.dictionary.com/browse/emotion>.

2 Encyclopedia Britannica, "Homeostasis," <https://www.britannica.com/science/homeostasis>.

3 Centers for Disease Control and Prevention, "CDC-Kaiser ACE Study," CDC.gov, <https://www.cdc.gov/violenceprevention/acestudy/about.html>.

4 Arjun Walia, "Nothing is Solid and Everything is Energy—Scientists Explain the World of Quantum Physics," Collective-evolution.com, <http://www.collective-evolution.com/2014/09/27/this-is-the-world-of-quantum-physics-nothing-is-solid-and-everything-is-energy/>.

5 Dooley, Mike, "The Law of Vibration," One-mind-one-energy.com, <http://www.one-mind-one-energy.com/Law-of-vibration.html>.

6 Dictionary.com, "Definition of frequency," <http://www.dictionary.com/browse/frequency>.

7 Stewart, David, PhD, "Are Chakras New Age?," *The Raindrop Messenger*, Vol. 11, No. 4. (Fall 2013) <http://www.raindroptraining.com/messenger/v11n4.html#newage>

8 McBride, Janet. *Scriptural Essence*, (Melville, NY: Cedar Hill Publishing, 2006), 11

9 Becker, Robert and Seldan, Gary, *The Body Electric*, (New York, NY: William Morrow Paperbacks, July 1998).

10 Dictionary.com, "Definition of light," <http://www.dictionary.com/browse/light>.

11 Gordon, Barry, “Can We Control Our Thoughts? Why Do Thoughts Pop into My Head as I’m Trying to Fall Asleep?,” Scientificamerican.com, <https://www.scientificamerican.com/article/can-we-control-our-thoughts/>.

12 Merriam-Webster.com, “Definition of word,” <https://www.merriam-webster.com/dictionary/word>.

13 Losier, Michael J, *Law of Attraction*, (New York, NY: Wellness Central Hachette Book Group, June 2007), 21

14 Truman, Karol, *Feelings Buried Alive Never Die*, (St. George, UT: Olympus Distributing, 2005), 273-278

15 Ledoux, JE, “Rationalizing Thoughtless Emotions,” *Insight* (Sept. 1989)

16 Stewart, David, PhD, *Healing Oils of the Bible*, (Marble Hill, MO: Care Publishing, April 2003), 26

17 Ross, Christina, *Etiology*, (Bloomington, IN: XLIBRIS Publishing, March 2013), 94.

18 YoungLiving.com, “Seed to Seal®,” <https://www.youngliving.com/en_US/discover/seed-to-seal>.

19 ReflexologyHistory.com, “The History of Reflexology,” <http://reflexologyhistory.com/History.html>.

20 Bauer, Brent, M.D, “What is Reflexology? Can it Relieve Stress?,” MayoClinic.org (September 2015,) <http://www.mayoclinic.org/healthy-lifestyle/consumer-health/expert-answers/what-is-reflexology/faq-20058139>.

21 Burroughs, Stanley, *Healing for the Age of Enlightenment*, (Snowball Publishing, 1993), 39.

22 Burroughs, 39-40

23 Oleson, Terry, *Auriculotherapy Manual: Chinese and Western Systems of Ear Acupuncture*, (London, United Kingdom: Churchill Livingstone, 2013).

24 Kurebayashi, Leonice and Silva, Maria, “Efficacy of Chinese Auriculotherapy for Stress in Nursing Staff: a Randomized Clinical Trial,” Pub Med Central® (May-June 2014), <https://www.ncbi.nlm.nih.gov/pmc/articles/PMC4292631/>.

25 Taipei Medical University, “Effect of Auricular Acupressure for Postpartum Insomnia: An Uncontrolled Clinical Trial,” Pub Med Central® (February 2016), <https://www.ncbi.nlm.nih.gov/pubmed/26612319>.

ADDITIONAL RECOMMENDED RESOURCES

Healing Oils of the Bible
by David Stewart, Ph.D.

The Biology of Belief
by Bruce Lipton

Feelings Buried Alive
by Karol Truman

Law of Attraction
by Michael Loiser

Releasing Emotional Patterns with Essential Oils
by Carolyn Mein, D.C.

Who Switched Off My Brain
by Dr. Carolyn Leaf

Heal Your Body
by Louise Hay

www.anointingnations.com

ABOUT THE AUTHOR

Rhonda's passion is assisting families with becoming more responsible and self-reliant for their health and well-being. This drive gave her a deeper understanding of the inherent value in Young Living Essential Oils. Rhonda quickly recognized that these oils were top quality and needed to be a part of everyone's daily wellness objectives.

Rhonda's essential oil journey began long before it was the "cool" thing to do. She chooses to use essential oils because they have a bioelectrical frequency that is several times greater than the frequency of herbs (dried or fresh), making them very potent. They are very diverse in their benefits and effects and can perform several different functions. Their energy and potency are unparalleled. For these reasons, they are Rhonda's first choice for supporting the body, mind, and spirit.

Rhonda has a Bachelor's Degree in Accounting, is a Doctor of Naturopathy, Aromatherapy Coach, Certified Raindrop Technique® Specialist, and a Certified Natural Health Practitioner, as well as a Master Herbalist.

INDEX

T

U

V

W

Y

Z

NOTES

To obtain additional copies and for more information on other books by Growing Healthy Homes, please visit our website at www.GrowingHealthyHomes.com

Nutrition 101: Choose Life!

Gentle Babies

Road to Royal: Roadmap to Success

Road to Wellness: Roadmap for a Lifestyle of Health

The ABC's of Building a Young Living Organization